Mice gnaw.

All Gone!

by Harriet Ziefert
pictures by Henrik Drescher

Harper & Row, Publishers

Deer nibble.

Raccoons   dine.

Seals gulp.

Kangaroos graze.

Anteaters snack.

Chimps feast.

Bears lunch.

Gorillas munch.

Giraffes...

swallow

slowly.

Cows chew.

Pigs slurp.